'Twas the Night Before CHRISTMAS

Clement Clarke Moore

Copyright © 2022

make believe ideas ltd

The Wilderness, Berkhamsted, Hertfordshire, HP4 2AZ, UK.
557 Broadway, New York, NY 10012, USA.

www.makebelieveideas.com

'Twas the night before Christmas, when all through the house
not a creature was stirring, not even a mouse.
The stockings were hung by the chimney with care,
in hopes that St. Nicholas soon would be there.

The children were nestled all **snug** in their beds,
while visions of **sugarplums** danced in their heads.

And **Mama** in her 'kerchief, and I in my cap,
had just settled down for a **long winter's** nap.

When out on the lawn there arose such a **clatter,**
I **sprang** from the bed to see what was the matter.
Away to the window
I **flew** like a **flash,**
tore open
the **shutters,** and
threw up
the **sash.**

The **moon**, on the breast of the new-fallen **snow**, gave the **luster** of midday to objects below. When, what to my **wondering** eyes should appear . . .

. . . but a miniature **sleigh** and eight tiny **reindeer**,
with a little **old** driver, so **lively** and quick,
I knew in a **moment** it must be **St. Nick.**

More **rapid** than eagles his **coursers** they came,
and he **whistled** and **shouted** and **called** them by **name**.

"Now, **Dasher!** Now, **Dancer!** Now, **Prancer** and **Vixen!**
On, **Comet!** On, **Cupid!** On, **Donner** and **Blitzen!**

To the top of the **porch!** To the top of the **wall!**
Now, **dash** away! Dash away! **Dash** away **all!**"

As dry **leaves** that before the **wild** hurricane fly,

when they **meet** with an obstacle, **mount** to the sky;

so up to the housetop the **coursers** they **flew**,

with the sleigh **full** of **toys**, and St. Nicholas, too.

And then, in a **twinkling**, I heard on the **roof**
the **prancing** and **pawing** of each little **hoof**.

As I **drew** in my head, and was turning around,
down the chimney St. Nicholas came with a **bound**.

He was **dressed** all in **fur**, from his **head** to his **foot**,
and his clothes were all **tarnished** with **ashes** and **soot**.

A bundle of **toys** was **flung** on his back,
and he looked like a **peddler** just **opening** his pack.

His eyes – how they **twinkled!** His dimples – how **merry!**

His **cheeks** were like **roses**, his nose like a **cherry!**

His **droll** little mouth was drawn up like a **bow**,

and the **beard** on his chin was as **white** as the **snow**.

He had a **broad** face and a little round **belly**
that **shook** when he **laughed**, like a bowlful of **jelly!**
He was **chubby** and **plump**, a right **jolly** old **elf,**
and I **laughed** when I saw him, in spite of myself.

A **wink** of his eye and a **twist** of his head soon gave me to know I had **nothing** to dread.

He spoke not a word,

but went straight to his work,

and filled all the **stockings;**

then turned

with a **jerk,**

and laying his **finger**

aside of his **nose**,

and giving a **nod**,

up the
chimney
he **rose!**

He sprang to his **sleigh**, to his **team** gave a **whistle**,
and away they all **flew**, like the down of a **thistle**.

But I heard him **exclaim**, as he drove out of sight,

"**Happy Christmas** to all,
and to **all** a **good night!**"